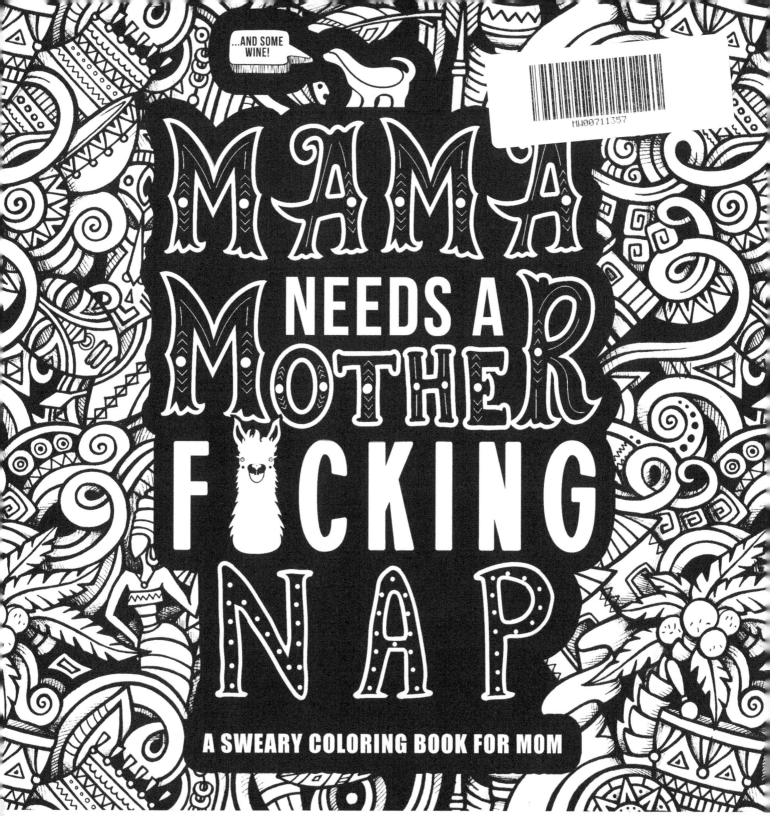

...AND SOME WINE!

MAMA NEEDS A MOTHER F*CKING NAP

A SWEARY COLORING BOOK FOR MOM

Want free goodies?
Email us at freebies@honeybadgercoloring.com

@honeybadgercoloring

Honey Badger Coloring

Shop our other books at
www.honeybadgercoloring.com

Wholesale distribution through Ingram Content Group
www.ingramcontent.com/publishers/distribution/wholesale

For questions and customer service, email us at
support@honeybadgercoloring.com

FREE PDF DOWNLOAD
OF THIS BOOK

www.honeybadgercoloring.com/mom

DOWNLOAD CODE:

NAP3793

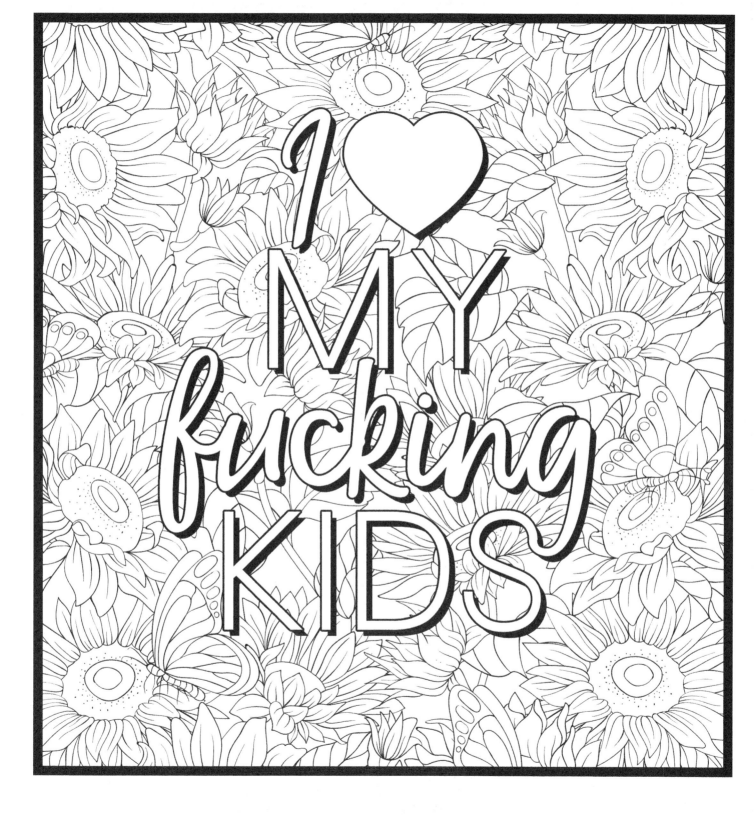

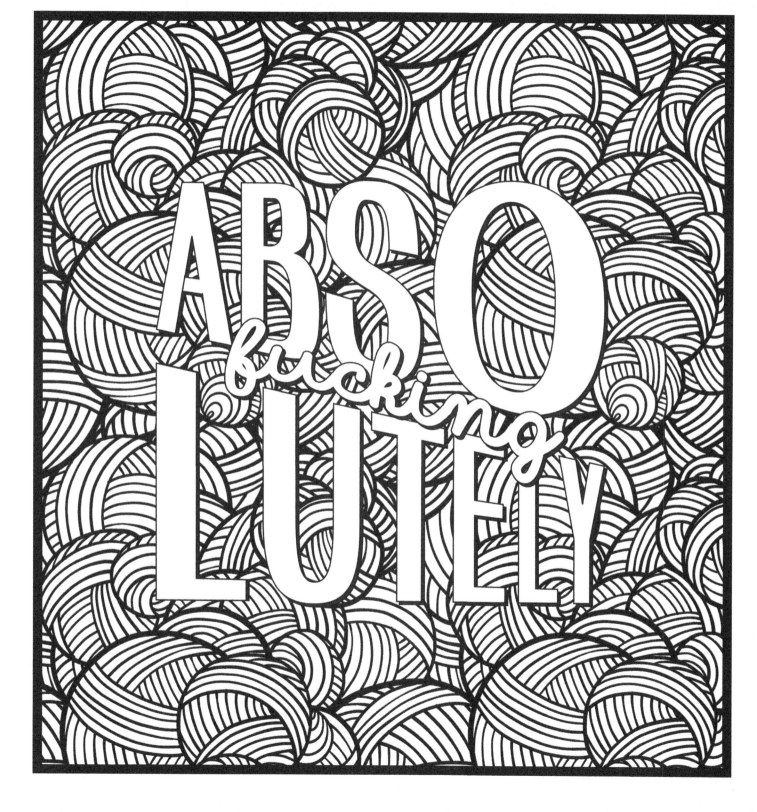

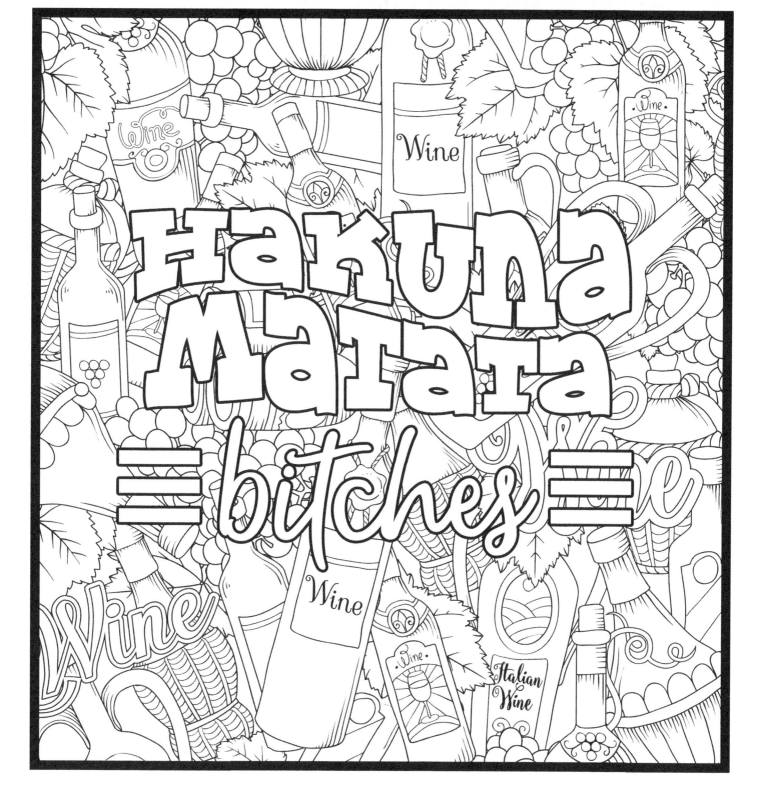

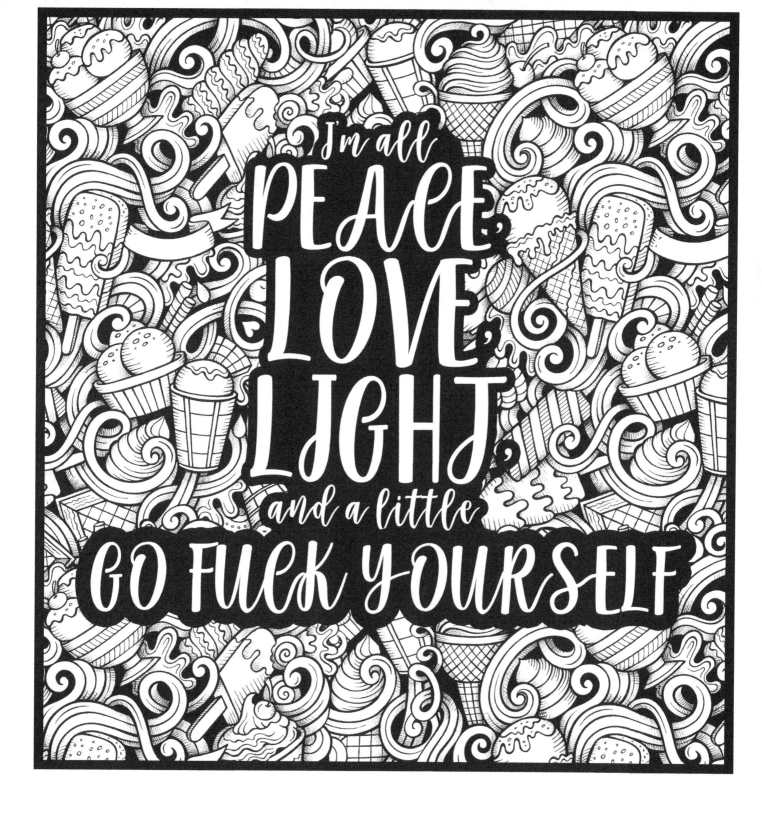

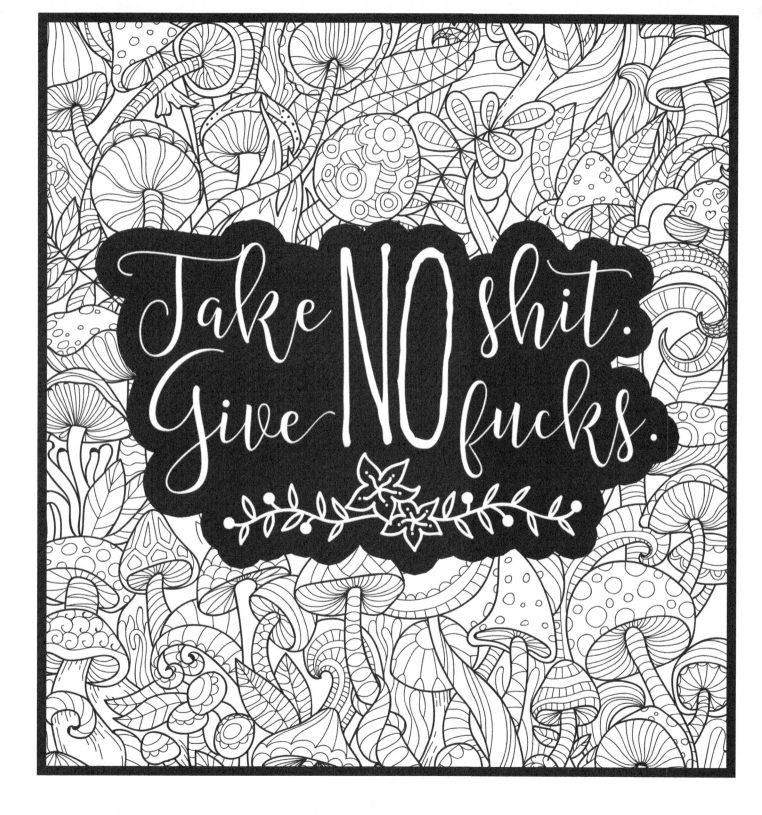

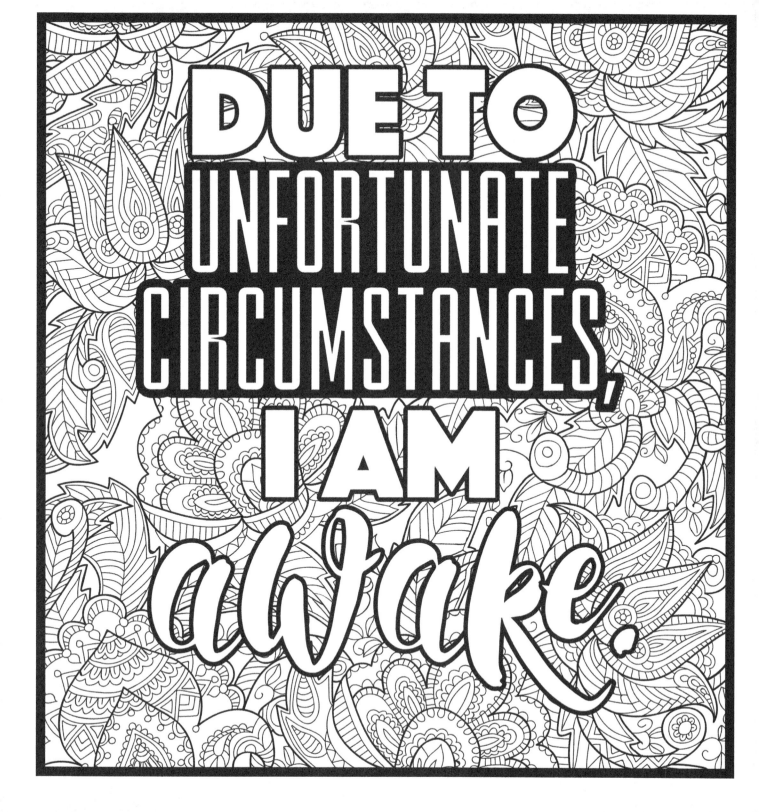

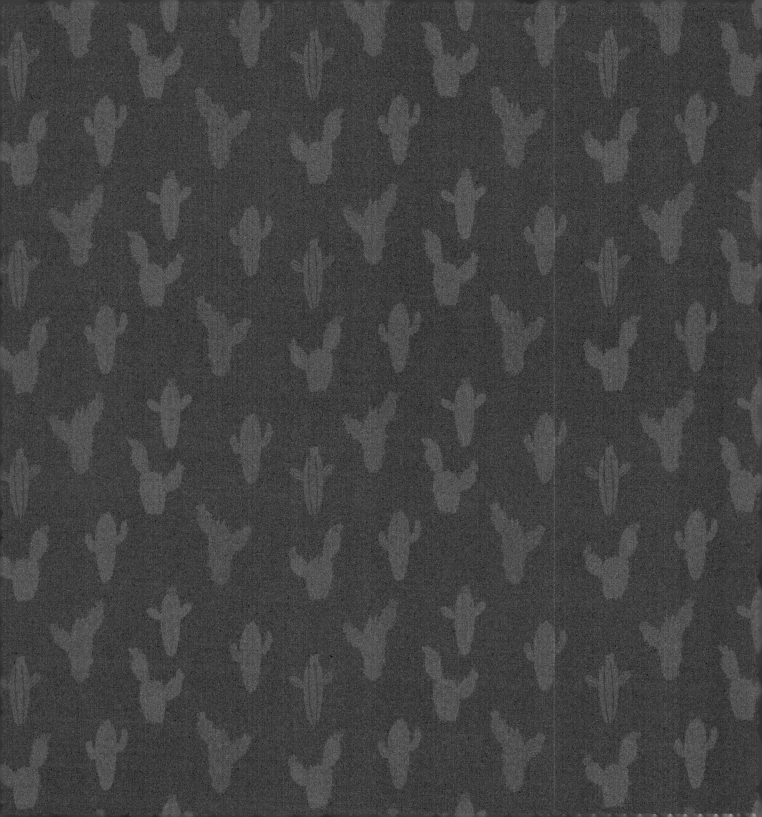

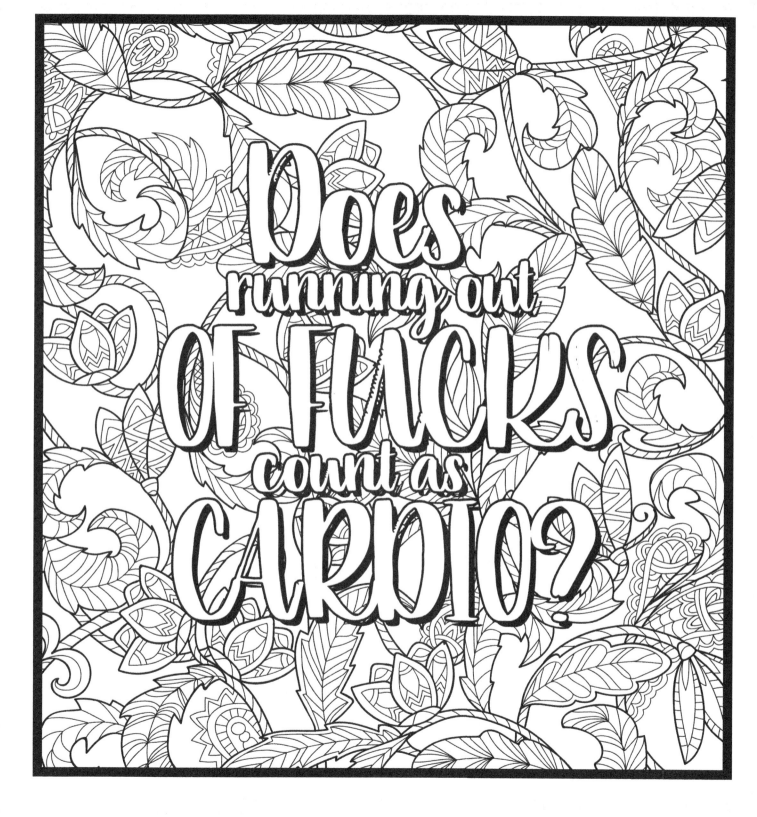

FREE PDF DOWNLOAD
OF THIS BOOK

DOWNLOAD CODE:

NAP3793

www.honeybadgercoloring.com/mom

Want free goodies?
Email us at freebies@honeybadgercoloring.com

@honeybadgercoloring

Honey Badger Coloring

Shop our other books at
www.honeybadgercoloring.com

Wholesale distribution through Ingram Content Group
www.ingramcontent.com/publishers/distribution/wholesale

For questions and customer service, email us at
support@honeybadgercoloring.com

Made in the USA
Coppell, TX
03 May 2020